THERE'S A MONKEY ON MY STREET

Illustrated by: Paul Miller

Written in partnership by:
Simcoe Muskoka District Health Unit,
Marketing Plus,
Simcoe Muskoka District Catholic School Board,
Simcoe County District School Board

© 2005 Simcoe Muskoka District Health Unit

This book belongs to:

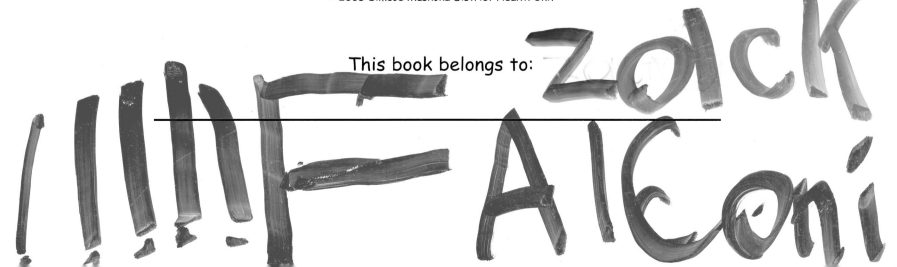

It was a sunny day. The kind of day Hannah loved. She could play outside with her older brother Jack. She could play with her new friend Little Monkey.

All the children in the neighbourhood came to play at Hannah's house.

Hannah got her tricycle for Little Monkey to ride. Little Monkey put his helmet on backwards.

"Oh no Little Monkey," said Hannah, "you have to put your helmet on properly."

Hannah showed Little Monkey the 2-4-1 helmet salute she learned in school.

Two fingers above the eyebrow
to the bottom of your helmet.

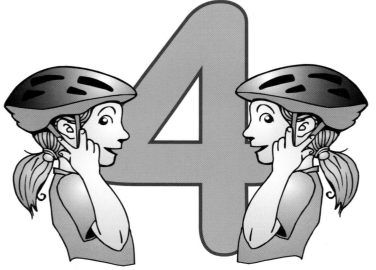

Four fingers to make a V-shape
around the bottom of your ears.

One finger under the strap beneath your chin.

Know your 2-4-1 helmet salute!

Parent Tip

►Young children can begin to learn about safety, but do not always understand or remember safety rules. Children this age still need adults to supervise them carefully.

Then off they went, riding up and down the driveway. All of the children followed and it looked like a parade with Hannah and Little Monkey leading the way.

Suddenly, Little Monkey began to ride out onto the street.

"Oh no Little Monkey! We're not allowed to ride on the street," said Hannah.

The walk signal appeared and Jack, Hannah and Little Monkey walked to the park.

At the park, Jack, Hannah and Little Monkey saw lots of children playing games and having fun. Little Monkey spotted a skateboard and excitedly jumped on.

"Oh no Little Monkey," said Hannah, "we have to wear the gear before we play on skateboards."

Hannah sings:

"Wrists and elbows, knees and head,
knees and head,
knees and head.
Wrists and elbows, knees and head,
wear the gear." (to the tune of Head and Shoulders)

Parent Tip

▸To prevent strangulation on play equipment remove all drawstrings from your child's clothing and teach your child to take off her bike helmet.

On the way home, Hannah and Little Monkey practised all of the safety rules they had learned.

Help Hannah and Little Monkey spot the children forgetting the safety rules.

1. Not wearing bike helmet riding bike. 2. Bike helmet straps not fastened and helmet too far back on head. 3. Riding bikes side by side. 4. Riding on left hand side of the street. 5. Crossing street at "Don't Walk" signal. 6. Young child crossing street without a parent. 7. Young child crossing street without holding hand of parent. 8. No parent supervising children on play equipment. 9. No helmet while riding tricycle. 10. Not wearing gear while scootering or skateboarding.

Help Hannah and Little Monkey spot the children remembering the safety rules.

1. Wearing bike helmet while riding. 2. Riding bikes in single file. 3. Older children riding on right hand side of the street. 4. Crossing street while crossing the street with a parent. 5. Holding hands while crossing the street at "Walk" signal. 6. Parent supervising at play equipment. 7. Wearing gear while scootering or skateboarding. 8. Child wearing helmet while riding tricycle. 9. Looking both ways before crossing the street.

The End.